I Push
I Pull

Susan M. Guthrie
Photographs by Ken O'Donoghue

I pull the big door.

You push the blue stroller.

3

I pull the red wagon.

You pull the big dog.

I push the wet sand.

I pull the duck toy.

I push the baby
in the blue swing.

13

I pull the red wagon.
You push the blue stroller.

15

I pull.
You push.